MW00423989

LONG-TERM
CARE INSURANCE

LONG-TERM CARE INSURANCE

How to Make Decisions That Are Right For You

Penelope S. Tzougros, PhD, ChFC, CLU

WEALTHY CHOICES®

Dr. Penelope S. Tzougros, ChFC, CLU
Financial Planner, Author, Host of Television's Money Makeover

*Wealthy Choices: The Seven Competencies
of Financial Success (Wiley)*

Annuities: Retirement Guarantees- Promises or Traps

How to Care for Mom When She's Miles Away

LifeWealth: Your Treasury

Wealthy Choices®
130 Turner Street, Building 3, Suite 230
Waltham, MA 02454

Email penelope@wealthychoices.com
Phone 781-893-0909 ext. 238
1-800-631-1970
Fax 781-893-3565

Financial Planning offered through Wealthy Choices® and Bay Financial Advisors, Inc.. Dr. Tzougros is also affiliated with Bay Financial Associates LLC (BFA).

Securities offered through LPL Financial, Member FINRA/SIPC.

Investment advice offered through Wealthy Choices® and Bay Financial Advisors, Inc., Registered Investment Advisors. Wealthy Choices® and Bay Financial Advisors, Inc. are separate entities from LPL Financial.

Special thanks to Glenn Cadigan, for collegial advice, Total Care Associates, Andover, MA; for graphic design, Timothy Blackburn; and for editing, Susan Kendrick, Susan Kendrick Write to Your Market, WI; and Francesca Scalzo, Toronto, Ontario.

ISBN: 978-0-9709870-0-6

To the memory of my beloved mother
whose radiant smile gave me the joy of life!

Author's
Welcome

Is your reaction to long-term care or "nursing home" insurance as it's often called, "I really don't want to think about it?" I do understand, which is why I've prepared this pocket guide for you. It is part of the conversation I would have with you if you were right here in my office.

Long-term Care Insurance is not something most of us want to think about. There are so many unknowns about what the future may hold, and seemingly endless options about how to prepare for it. Nevertheless, now is the time to begin making choices, while you still have the time and resources to decide what you really want for yourself or a loved one.

Whether you are single or part of a couple or just helping someone else, consider this pocket guide the conversation that will start you off in the right direction. Many clients who come to me for financial planning ask the very same questions that I address here. Your questions may be similar, and so the answers will help you think through your own concerns related to long-term care. It's a significant decision that will deeply affect you and your family.

INTRODUCTION

Deciding What's Right for You

It is important to understand that how you make—or neglect to make—important life decisions right now will determine the kind of life choices you will have available later on.

WHAT IS YOUR DECISION-MAKING STYLE?

When you have to make a decision about something that worries you and you don't want to think about it anyway, do you often hear the same ideas circling in your head? Do you feel trapped by the repetition of worry or pieces of information? Or, once an issue gets your attention, are you more likely to gather a lot of information and become knowledgeable? Does that knowledge make you feel overwhelmed? Does it help you act with confidence? Whatever your style and success in decision making is, this guide will help you sort out the debate you might be having with yourself or others.

What If...

If you knew, absolutely, that out of every two people one would need long-term care services,[1] and that person was you, what would you do?

Would you purchase the insurance?

If it were free, would you apply for it?

You might be surprised to find that there are a variety of answers that people give to those two questions. The fact that not everyone automatically answers "yes" means that these are complex and often emotional issues. They are not just about dollars and cents. If you weren't absolutely sure that you would need long-term care, but your health was good enough now to qualify for long-term care insurance, why would you apply for it? My assumption here is that a friend said something in casual conversation, or you saw an advertisement, or you've just heard about someone going into a nursing home. Some mention of long-term care may have made just enough of an impression for you to have stored a mental response about it. So take a minute to recall that response. It may even be the reason you picked up this pocket guide. Jot down any reasons you might apply for such coverage.

Are your ideas similar to what others have said? Check the ones below that you agree with. Maybe make two check marks for any that are important to you.

- *I don't want to be a burden to anyone.*
- *I want to be independent.*
- *I don't want to use up the money I've saved to leave to my (spouse, children, grandchildren, friend, charity, etc).*
- *I want to have the insurance pay my bills instead of pulling money out of my own income, savings or investments.*

- *I want to be able to choose what services I would have available to me and what facility I go to, instead of being assigned by an agency.*
- *I don't have anyone nearby who could take care of me on a daily basis.*
- *I don't know if I have enough money for my lifetime. I want a backup to pay big bills, like long-term care.*
- *I don't want to be on welfare.*

By answering those questions, you've explained to yourself why you might want the insurance. If you owned it, you might feel satisfied because it was in place to pay certain bills and you would have some control of your choices. However, if you did not check off any of the eight items, you might say comfortably, "I don't need it. I will spend the money I have saved and pay for my own care. No one else in my family or close circle needs my money. When I have spent down my money, then I will be eligible for whatever services are offered by the government or my community." What if you are in the middle? You have some reasons you want the coverage, but still feel unsure if it is right for you. Please keep reading.

WHEN DO YOU NEED TO DECIDE?

If you are over age 50, you should be looking at these choices for your own situation. If you are under age 50, you should be creating a conversation with older relatives about what worries them, what is important to them if their health should become compromised, and how they want you to be supportive of them.

THE GOAL OF THIS GUIDE

The goal of this guide is to help you explore a complex issue and make choices that you and your family members can live with—now and in the future. It gives you support and information, helps you watch out for your dollars, and removes worry. The best outcome will be that you feel confident about making an informed choice—whatever that choice is.

How This Pocket Guide Is Organized to Help You

INTRODUCTION — DECIDING WHAT'S RIGHT FOR YOU

This section discusses the importance of your decision-making style and how the decisions you make now will impact your future.

PART ONE — WHAT IS LONG-TERM CARE, WHO NEEDS IT, AND WHO PAYS FOR IT?

The first part of this guide focuses on your life circumstances to help you determine if you would benefit from owning long-term care insurance. You may decide to stop reading at the end of Part One because it has untangled the issue for you and you are ready to choose. If your decision is to apply for coverage, you'll want to become familiar with the concepts in Part Two.

PART TWO — DESIGNING A POLICY TO FIT YOUR NEEDS

The second part of this guide explains, from a financial planning point of view, what you need to know to design a policy correctly: which provisions are most critical, when to buy, how much you should expect to pay, and more.

PART ONE

What Is Long-Term Care,
Who Needs It, and Who Pays for It?

WHAT IS LONG-TERM CARE?

Long-term care covers a wide range of services, including care given in your home, a nursing home, an adult day-care center, and in assisted living.

Long-term care also covers a range of services,

1

including personal care, speech therapy, occupational therapy and even light housekeeping. There is often a provision in the contract to modify your house with things like a wheelchair ramp, or grab bars in a bathroom. In many policies, there is "respite care" which allows an informal caregiver—a member of the family who has been caring for you—to have some "vacation" time while someone else is paid to take on those duties.

Long-term care can also fill in the gaps between what you can and cannot do for yourself. What if you couldn't do normal daily activities like bathing, dressing, or getting out of a chair, but you were still a whiz at your favorite pastimes: playing cards, quilting, fundraising for your favorite organization, surfing the internet, or playing chess by email? Wouldn't it be useful to have some help with what you couldn't do by yourself? The insurance designed to cover the costs of such help just described is long-term care insurance.

WHO NEEDS LONG-TERM CARE?

Who Currently Receives It?

In 2013, about 12 million Americans received long-term care. About 2 million received care in a nursing home or a residential care community, while the others received care through adult day-care centers, hospice and home health agencies.[2] About 52 million caregivers attend to the needs of those 18 and older who have cognitive and functional limitations. Thirty percent of those caregivers were themselves over 65.[3]

In addition to the 6.7 million over 65 who need care, there are 5.4 million working age people, and about 600,000 children who are receiving care in nursing homes and in the community.[4] According to the Report to Congress from the Commission on Long-Term Care, by 2050, 27 million will need care, which more than doubles the current levels.[5]

For those over 65, "the lifetime probability of becoming disabled in at least two activities of daily living or being cognitively impaired is 68%".[6] Of those age 75 and older, the estimate is that three out of five will be in a nursing home.[7]

About 25% of people need a facility for a period of time and are then back to their normal lives. Another 42% have multiple admissions over time.[8]

Will You Provide Long-Term Care for Someone Else?

Currently, one in five American households provide informal care to a relative or friend over the age of 50.[9] "The value of family caregiving exceeds the total value of all paid LTSS [Long-term Services and Supports]."[10]

The typical informal caregiver is a woman, age 48, who, in addition to working outside the home, spends at least 20.4 hours—the equivalent of a part-time job—as a caregiver. At least 66% of caregivers are women.[11] Because this could be you, it's important to look directly at what the care scene is like.

Please answer the questions below:

- Who have you nursed?
- Have you nursed an adult?
- If you are a petite woman, could you manage to lift a taller, heavier adult and turn him or her in bed?

- Could you bathe that person?

If this responsibility is likely to fall on you, what are your options? Consider how having long-term care insurance would help both you and the person you're caring for.

How Would Your Life Change?

Completing the questions in this section will help you think about your daily routines and how they might be altered by needing care for six months or more. It doesn't matter why you were incapacitated, whether it was a stroke, a terrible accident or some disease. For the sake of this set of exercises, you have to imagine yourself bed-ridden or severely restricted in your normal abilities and activities.

Visualize How Things Could Be

If you have had the blessing of good health, it may be hard to imagine yourself restricted. Try things like writing with your other hand, as if your opposite side had stopped functioning because of a stroke. Use just one arm for most of the day. Try walking around with ear plugs in your ears to simulate hearing loss.

Rub Vaseline on your eyeglasses. If you don't wear glasses, buy an inexpensive pair of reading glasses or sunglasses and rub Vaseline on them.

Whichever of these exercises you try, monitor your emotional reaction and your physical adaptation. Were you less patient? More depressed? Angry? Did you feel left out? Yes, it is frightening to see yourself or someone you love compromised. Pushing your imagination may help you face the long-term care issue and make a decision. Whatever that decision is, it should be yours by choice, not neglect. That is, it should be one you make for yourself, not one that is made for you because you waited too long.

If you are engaged by these simulations and want to see a video of an amazing high tech approach to understanding our changing bodies, check endnote 12.

Evaluating Your Current Needs and Level of Future Care

Please answer the questions below:

- Does anyone live with you?
- Who would walk your dog or take care of similar daily responsibilities?

- Who would do your grocery shopping and prepare meals?

- Does a friend or family member live close enough to be able to stop by once a day? Twice a day? For how long on each visit?

- For how long could that person alter his or her own work and family routines to help you?

- Would you accept this person's help with your banking business?

- Would you trust that person with handling your money?

- Would you rather pay an accountant, lawyer or some other professional to handle your financial affairs if you were unable to act on your own behalf?

- Would you be comfortable with a family member or friend helping you bathe and dress?

- Would you be more comfortable having a trained professional—nurse, doctor, or nurse's aide—help you?

- Is there a trained professional in your inner circle who would be able to serve as your nurse or aide?

- Do you laugh easily? Could you make light of other people's mistakes or their not showing up when they said?

- Have you ever lived in a dorm, barracks or camp? Was it easy for you to adapt to it? What did you like? What didn't you like?

- What are your rules of privacy? *"I don't like people knowing my business about... I am most private about..."*

- Have you ever had a prolonged illness when others pitched in to help? What did they do for you? Were you comfortable with that?

- Do you normally ask others for help? Are you comfortable asking others for help?

Having thought through these questions, are you more like Profile One than Profile Two?

1. **Profile One** I like my personal and financial privacy and do not want others to know my business. I prefer professional care.

2. **Profile Two** I feel like I am part of a big, reciprocating network of family and friends. I would have plenty of help on a regular basis

and would be very comfortable receiving that help.

If you are more like Profile One than Profile Two, formal arrangements might suit you. You might want to own long-term care insurance, which could help pay for some of that formal help.

If you're more like Profile Two and very easy about family and friends nursing you, just as you have nursed them, then you might be able to rely on an informal tag team of helpers. If you are more like Profile Two, but your loved ones have erratic schedules, are not nearby or cannot be with you often because of busy careers or because the kind of care you need is beyond their skill, then you may have to use professional services. Again, this would be easier to afford with the help of a privately held long-term care policy.

Profiles One and Two are two ends of the spectrum. Your preferences may lie somewhere in between, so you would be likely to mix and match the care you need from friends, family, government programs and private long-term care insurance.

WHO PAYS FOR LONG-TERM CARE?

You may stay perfectly healthy until you die at age 105. I hope you do. But you may very well develop a serious, long-term disability from arthritis, diminished vision, a heart condition, diabetes or some other health problem, so you definitely need to understand the financial implications of this possibility.

A worst-case scenario would be needing care 24 hours a day for a lifetime, like someone who has had a spinal cord injury from a car accident or sports injury. This is frightening to contemplate! Such care could cost between $91,250 to over $300,000 a year. [13]

Even if you were a millionaire, how long would your money last at that rate of additional expense? Does your health insurance policy have unlimited benefits? Are there restrictions on the type of care your health insurance will provide? Let's take a look at who provides and pays for various kinds of long-term care.

Government Plans

Would Medicare Pay for You?

You would probably use up all available benefits from Medicare within six months because Medicare is not designed to pay for the kind of long-term care, or "custodial" care, needed in cases of Alzheimer's disease, stroke, and many other chronic conditions. It is designed primarily to handle short-term acute and recovery care.

Medicare is designed for skilled care, which means care available to you 24 hours a day when it is ordered by a doctor and provided by skilled medical personnel such as a registered nurse or professional therapist. The first 20 days are covered after you pay a deductible. Then you co-pay for the next 80 days. There is a one-time lifetime benefit added. Then you have the usual Medicare reimbursements.

Would Medicaid Pay for You?

Yes, Medicaid is very likely to pay if you are a single person with $2,000 or less of "countable assets" as Medicaid defines them. Once a snapshot is taken of a couple's assets, the community spouse can keep half of the couple's countable assets that were in that snapshot. In 2016, that amount is $119,200.[14] (This figure changes periodically). You qualify for Medicaid according to specific guidelines regarding your financial resources. The rules are complex and differ from state to state. They are designed to cover those who have few assets and no other resources or options. It is not for those who have decided to try to hide their assets to become eligible.

Middle-class and well-to-do individuals who try to circumvent the system will find that there are penalties involved. Medicaid representatives are specifically trained to be on the lookout for such inappropriate schemes.

"Self" Insurance

How Would Your Savings Hold Up?

What if you are not in need of acute care as the result of an accident or illness? Medicare would not be involved. If you have assets well above the Medicaid limits, it will not pay for care either.

So how would you pay for care if you were diagnosed with senile dementia or Alzheimer's or if you had a stroke which left you paralyzed on one side? You could pay for services out of your own savings, but how might that affect you?

Let's use the national average for the cost of a year in a nursing home, which is about $91,250, or

$250 daily.[15] The average stay is two and a half years. However, the Commission on Long-Term Care Report to Congress estimates long-term services and supports (LTSS) will be needed for more than five years by 20% of those 65 and older; 20% will be in the facility for two to five years, 12% for one to two years, and 17% will need only one year of care.[16]

Since at this point in our medical knowledge a person suffering the effects of Alzheimer's or a stroke is unlikely to be reversed back to perfect health, how many years at about $91,250 a year would your current savings and investments pay for? How long would your savings last if part of the bill were paid by a long-term care policy?

- If you are used to a more affluent lifestyle and/or live in a more expensive urban area, the cost for a nursing home could begin at $383 or $435 a day, or $139,580 to $158,775 a year.[17] When would your money run out?

- Suppose that instead of a perpetual stay you had the average stay of two and a half years in an average facility for a total cost of about $228,125. If you spent that much out of your investments, how would that affect your own retirement nest egg? Would it wipe out all your savings?

- Would you have to work longer or return to work?
- Would you have to scale down your standard of living?
- Would it be a very small percentage of your portfolio and therefore of no consequence?

So far we've asked what would happen if you had to cover your own expenses because your circumstances didn't fit Medicare or Medicaid guidelines, and you didn't own a long-term care policy.

What If You Don't Buy the Insurance?

What if you just saved more money? What if instead of paying an insurance premium, of say $300 a month (premiums vary widely based on 12 key factors), you were able to invest that same dollar amount in some hypothetical investment that earned an average annualized return of 8%?[18] How much might you have accumulated at the end of 20 years? Maybe about $176,706 before taxes.

Would it cover the average stay described in the previous paragraph which we speculated might be $228,125? No. You saved for 20 years and still came up short, especially on an after-tax basis. And of course, there is no guarantee that your need for care would coincide with your bank account being big enough to cover the need. So self-insuring, relying on the money you save instead of using an insurance policy, would require that you guess right about how much money you should save and when the catastrophe would hit you. If you are part of a couple, the matter could be even more complicated because it is not unusual to have each person needing some level of care.

Saving to Self-insure Versus Paying a Premium

Which of these two options would work better for you, not just financially, but also psychologically?

1. **Option 1** Self-insuring: You save the $176,706 we just talked about, but are worried about spending it because you have no other back-up. Would it frustrate you or comfort you to have the "frozen" money that you couldn't use for anything else?

2. **Option 2** Paying a premium: You spend the monthly premium for a policy and know that whatever happens, you have a plan of action and some level of protection in place so that the rest of your nest egg will probably not be spent for this purpose. You would feel you had freedom to use your money. It wasn't frozen.

If you spent $3,600 a year in premiums and were entitled to about $91,250 of care, the premiums would be paying, in any year of care, 3.94% of your cost of care. You could say that your premium dollars were helping you free up your other savings. The insurance policy would be giving you leverage to handle a potentially large bill. It's like the leverage you use when you put down a down payment on a home that is many times more valuable than the down payment.

Which option fits the way you see things? Are you a good saver? Do you like to have alternatives? Do you like leveraging your money, making it do more for you?

Insurance Companies

What If You Decide to Own Long-Term Care Insurance?

Now let's put a safety net under you, meaning that you own some long-term care insurance. Suppose you paid a long-term care insurance premium of $300 a month for 20 years; you would get your money's worth if you were in care for just 158 days. Anything over 158 days would exceed the roughly $72,000 in paid premiums.

If you experienced the average stay of two and a half years, you would have "gotten your money's worth" many times over. If you like a good deal, read the next three sentences, but if you don't like arithmetic, skip them. The premiums you paid for over 20 years might have totaled $72,000. Supposing that the cost of care increased by 3% per year, then nursing home cost might have risen from $91,250 to $166,143. All those premiums you paid would have covered only about 44% of the cost of one year's care.

If in twenty years, you were to be in a nursing home for three years, and the cost of care has continued to rise at 3%, the facility cost for those three years might have been $513,530. IF you paid premiums for 21 to 23 years, your outlay might have been $82,800, which would have been only 16.13% of the cost of care. Your choice to buy insurance would have provided care at a "discount"; you leveraged your money in a good way.[19] More importantly, you maintained your independence longer.

Family Considerations

If you cannot afford the premium, but your children or another person wants to purchase and pay for a policy for you, please accept the help. They would ensure that help is on the way, even though they themselves might not be able to be with you as much as they would like. In a loving family, caring about and for each other is a joint effort.

Working on a strategy before a crisis would give everyone peace of mind. In families that are separated by geography or emotional difficulties, maybe there is even more reason to have a back-up plan that shifts the responsibility for care to professionals instead of one reluctant family member. If you are not alone, long-term care is ultimately a family decision. If you are alone in your responsibility for yourself, then it is squarely your decision.

Do *Not* Buy Insurance If...

Do not buy insurance if your personal feelings, financial situation and family circumstances fit the guidelines in this section. Although the topic of long-term care may make you feel like a compendium of potential medical disasters that may or may not materialize, I am not forgetting your resilience and capacity for love, laughter, worries and complaints. I see you as a treasury of emotions, values, thoughts and concerns and this section reflects that view.

Suppose that you would definitely need care, you could afford the insurance, and you could qualify for it. It still might not be the right choice for you. Why? Because some combination of privacy concerns, your temperament, income, assets and family support might indicate that you may be better off with other arrangements.

For example, if it is unthinkable to you to be in an institutional environment in which people can interfere with how you organize your time, where your surroundings are aesthetically distressing, and you are surrounded by people not of your choosing, then being able to afford a care facility, even a very nice one, will be unacceptable to you. You might also be unwilling to have a "stranger" taking care of you at home. Hopefully, you are fortunate enough to have a large, loving family or network of friends all living close by that can create a constant rotation of help which could meet all your needs.

Be aware, however, that counting on just one person or even a couple to meet your needs may not be realistic. It is important to determine if that person will be able to pursue what is necessary for his or her own life and take care of you. Does the person have the time, physical ability, devotion, financial resources and a basic knowledge of nursing?

If you don't have enough family or friends nearby who can and will take care of you, you will probably find yourself paying for private duty nurses, aides and/or a live-in companion. Keep in mind, however, that one eight-hour shift a day for a Home Health Aide might cost $20 an hour or $160 a day; that would mean $41,600 for the year for just one shift five days a week. A Home Health Aide does not provide medical care.[20]

In evaluating your options for choosing and paying for long-term care, it's important to balance all your financial needs and personal preferences as much as possible. In this way you can arrive at a truly workable and comfortable solution to your potential long-term care needs.

Can You Afford Long-Term Care Insurance?

You can determine whether you need or want long-term care insurance by evaluating your responses to the information and questions presented so far. The issue now becomes, if you have decided that this insurance should be part of your safety net, how much of it can you appropriately afford?

What Might the Policy Cost?

In one sense, it doesn't matter what a policy costs. If it is not the right solution for you, it doesn't matter what it costs or how much extra money you have to spend on it. Likewise, if it is the right solution for you, it doesn't matter what it costs because over the years you probably "found" the money to do whatever was necessary, like fix the roof, have dental work, etc.

In many cases, depending on your age and other factors, $100 to $1,000 or more a month will set up some kind of program for you. Insurance policies, like houses, can be designed in many different ways with a variety of features and benefits. The following questions will help you sort out the dollars and cents of your decision.

Key Questions: Income Guidelines

Whatever the premium is for a policy that is tailored to your circumstances, could you afford the premium now without cutting back on other necessities like food, medicine and exercise classes?

Premiums are expected to be level, but under certain circumstances they can increase. Insurers offer guaranteed renewable policies, which means that as long as you, the insured, continue to pay the premium, the insurer will not cancel the policy. However, the insurer also says that if it increases the premium for the whole class of policies, then your premium will increase. Could you afford the premium even if there was a 10% to 20% increase?

Are your income sources increasing yearly so that they keep up with inflation? Social Security has an adjustment for inflation, but most company pensions do not have a cost-of-living adjustment. If you answered "yes" to all three questions, then it may make sense for you to apply for coverage. You may read some articles that say that if you have less than $25,000 of annual income you probably should not purchase this insurance. That annual income figure is not terribly helpful, because the issue is not how much income you have, but how much you have left after you pay your bills and the normal extras. That is why answering "yes" to those three questions is a much more important guide as to whether the insurance is appropriate for you.

HOW MUCH INCOME DO YOU NEED?

This set of questions explores how much income you have left after you pay your bills. Please answer the following questions about your cash flow:

- Are you currently working?
- Is working optional?
- What would happen financially if you stopped?
- What does it cost you to live monthly?
- How much money is left after necessary expenses and normal extras?
- Is there enough left to pay for care out-of-pocket?
- What is the average cost per day of a nursing home in your area? (Visit a few of them to correlate the cost, and your impressions of the facility. Could you live there?)
- What is the average hourly cost of a skilled nurse visiting your house? A nurse's aide? A physical therapist? (Calling a few services may give you a realistic sense of these expenses.)

Given the research you just did, could you afford to have professional care? How much care could you afford? Two hours a day? Ten hours a day? Suppose it cost an average of $20 an hour. What could you budget for care and/or for the premium for a long-term care policy? What additional income can your investments produce?

Now let's take a look at paying for care, or a policy by using income from your assets and investments. The central question is not the size of your portfolio, but what it is doing for you. It is not how high your net worth is but how it is structured. Net worth means what you own minus what you owe. If your net worth is $2 million but most of that is in homes that you do not rent, then your real estate does not produce income for you. You could have money in a variety of investments that may grow in value but do not produce current income. You might be "rich," but feel like you have no money to spend.

You see the problem.

For now you may just want to scan the next questions, keeping them in mind for later when you can make a careful analysis of your portfolio:

- If your net worth is a mix of assets that produce income and assets that do not, how much could you withdraw to pay for your care?

- Could you change the asset balance to achieve more income and still have the appropriate growth?

- Could you sell off assets to pay for your care? By how much could you reduce your assets and still have them provide the inflation-adjusted income you need for normal living expenses?

- Could your portfolio continue to generate the necessary income for everyday life if you withdrew $100,000? $250,000? $500,000? $1,000,000? If you could reduce your portfolio by these significant amounts, and it could still generate the income you needed to live on and pay for care, then you are not likely to need a long-term care policy.

The central question is not the size of your portfolio, or how much your net worth is, but what your holdings are doing for you. You may need help figuring out the answer, but this is the question to focus on.

CAN YOU HAVE TOO MUCH MONEY?

Can you have too much money to bother with long-term care insurance? Maybe. If you have about $4 million in income-producing assets, you probably would self-insure. But that decision depends on what you are trying to do with your money and how much money you need to support your current life-style. Do you want to live on the income without spending the principal? Do you intend to leave a large bequest to loved ones and/or charity? If you answered "yes" to those two questions, your portfolio might be stretched if it had to pay for long-term care for an extended period of time.

A simple example:

If $4 million were invested and earned a hypothetical total return of 8% on an average annualized basis, you might have about $192,000 after 40% taxes. Could the portfolio spin out another $100,000 or more to pay for long-term care, or would you reduce your lifestyle by $100,000? [21]

SUMMARY OF INCOME ISSUES

Whether you have millions or not, the key questions are the same:

1. What is the surplus after you pay for necessities and niceties? If there is enough, fine, maybe a policy makes sense. If there isn't a surplus now or in the foreseeable future, do not buy a policy.

2. What else are you trying to do with your money? Take care of your spouse or significant other? Pass it on? Live only on the principal? A long-term care policy may help you achieve multiple goals.

3. Could you maintain your lifestyle if you were to sell off a significant portion of your holdings to pay for care that extended for many years? Would you prefer to do that than purchase a policy?

ESTATE PLANNING AND OTHER LEGAL CONSIDERATIONS

Up until now the focus has been on you, not on those close to you. What happens to them during a period of your receiving long-term care? What happens after your death?

Your decision affects you and any one very close to you, whether they are blood relations or not. If you use up your investment portfolio on long-term care costs, what happens to your spouse or significant other? What happens to the nest egg that was supposed to support the retirement of two people?

If you decide to purchase long-term care insurance, how you design that policy relates to the bigger picture of what happens to your current assets and what is left for someone else.

The policy is only one piece of your estate and financial planning. You will still need to discuss various other issues with an attorney. Who should own what asset? Who should be the beneficiary of each asset? Which of the following documents will you need drawn or revised: a will, a durable power of attorney, a health care proxy, a living will, a living trust, or other trusts? These legal documents make sure that assets are there for your use even if you cannot speak for yourself. After your passing, the documents carry out your wishes. They give you control before and after death.

Will You or Your Family Lose Your House?

If you were expecting that the value of your home would take care of your loved ones when you died, it is very, very important for you to know that if you were cared for by Medicaid, the value of those services will be recovered from your home after your death when the house is sold. A lien is put on your home.

Yes, there are some protections for your family, but in Massachusetts there is a very special protection.

It is a significant reason to purchase long-term care insurance. In Massachusetts, if you purchase a long-term care policy with a $125 a day benefit of two years, and it is not drawn on before you enter a nursing home, Medicaid will not put a lien on your home. The state takes your purchase of the policy as a good faith effort to cover your own costs.

Check your state. Does it have a similar arrangement?

DO YOU QUALIFY FOR LONG-TERM CARE INSURANCE?

Take an objective look at your health. Are you healthy enough to qualify for the insurance coverage? Some insurance companies have a straightforward accept-or-reject approach. Others may offer to insure you but "rate" the policy. That means that they will charge more per unit of coverage. For example, a company may not decline coverage for an insulin-dependent diabetic. The insurer may say instead, "We can cover you, but the cost will reflect the added medical risk of your having diabetes."

You might be surprised to learn that a person who has a medical history that includes a cancer operation, for example, may still qualify for insurance. Of course, each situation is individually evaluated when a person applies for coverage and the insurer reviews the reports from doctors. To evaluate your medical condition through the eyes of the insurer, make a list of the medications you are taking, the dosage, and the condition being treated. Then call an agent who is knowledgeable about long-term care insurance. That person can make preliminary inquiries to see if you would be considered insurable.

As we age, we are less likely to be insurable. Here are the statistics for those who were disappointed and who had to find a different plan of action. Age groups of those declined coverage in 2012: 17% of those in the 50's, 25% of those in their 60's, and 45% of those in their 70's, and 80% of those 80 and older.[22]

At younger ages, not only are you more likely to be insurable, but you may qualify for better rates because you are healthy. With the same policy design, the premium for the 60 year old is about 52% less than that for a 70 year old. Procrastination can be costly. By not making an early decision, you may eliminate long-term care insurance as a possible solution as your health changes or the premium becomes too high.

PART TWO

Designing a Policy To Fit Your Needs

If you have decided that you want the protection of a long-term care insurance policy, you need to know how to design it to suit you and the needs of other family members immediately affected by your incapacity. This section gives you the questions you need to ask and the provisions you'll want to consider as you make specific choices about your long-term care policy.

Points of Comparison

There are about twenty points of comparison in policies. In addition, there may be special items that are tacked on to distinguish a particular insurance company's offering. Our goal here is not to cover every point, but rather to introduce a way of thinking about designing a policy that has merit as part of your financial plan.

None of us insures against every catastrophe. Most of us do not keep up the maximum on even our house and car insurances, which are mandatory coverages. We are always on the lookout for prudent choices and a good use of our dollars. I will state what I think would be a most helpful policy design and it will be up to you, your advisor and your checkbook to move in that direction if it seems right for you.

A Word About Group Policies

Group policies that may be offered through your workplace are not likely to offer the same provisions that individual policies offer. Group policies may be more expensive, and usually less comprehensive, with less opportunity to tailor them to your needs.[23] That doesn't mean you should dismiss them. It means that it is a different product designed for a specific group purpose. Look at what it offers, not just the price tag, or the convenience of payroll sign-up.

Group insurance does have one advantage. If your health is already compromised, you may be able to enter a group contract with fewer medical questions. Group insurance may be your only choice.

UPDATES

Long-term care insurers are in a continuous process of listening to the consumer, learning from claims filed, responding to medical advances, adhering to new regulations and, therefore, changing their offerings. If you examined policies even a year or two ago, you will find that many of them have already changed and that some features have been removed and others have been added.

New provisions are in the works. If you want an update, or a review of your current contract, speak to the insurance company that issued your contract, your financial advisor, call me at 781-893-0909, ext. 238, or 1-800-631-1970, or email me at penelope@ wealthychoices.com.

A FINANCIAL PLANNER'S APPROACH TO POLICY DESIGN:

The features 1 through 15 (inflation rider) are the most critical elements. Various features from 16 on may be nice to have but not worth sacrificing the more critical elements of the policy. You may have to trade off one feature for another because of the cost, your health or the availability of the policy in your state. I have deliberately not been adamant about what is "best" because, after years of counseling individuals, I know that what is "best" varies in each special set of circumstances. Nonetheless, my suggestions are strong, and your phone is nearby. Remember, if you want to, you can talk with your current valued advisors, or call me at 1-800-631-1970. In any case, I'm confident that if you keep your focus on your major reasons for owning this protection, you will make good choices for the policy design.

1. *A Comprehensive Policy*

Because most people would rather be cared for at home, purchase a policy that covers at-home care as well as care in a facility like a nursing home, adult day-care, or assisted living.

2. *A "Bucket"*

Today, policies are designed so that there is one "bucket" of money which you can dip into to pay for at-home care, nursing home care or other services. Some older policies have two buckets, and you can use the money for only one type of care or the other. The one bucket, or pooled benefit, is more flexible and the more useful approach. How much to buy? A long-term care insurance policy covers the cost of a day of care at home or in a facility like a nursing home. Daily benefits currently range from $50 to $500 a day, and you can choose any amount. As I said earlier, check to see what the costs are in your area, then decide if you want to keep costs down by co-paying. In this case, co-paying means that if a facility near you costs $160 a day, you may want to purchase a benefit of $80 a day. The other $80 would come from your savings or investments. This strategy helps you reduce the premium. If you wanted the whole $160 paid, you could purchase that size benefit instead.

3. *At-Home Benefit*

Most policies allow you to have a dollar benefit for home care that is as much as the dollar benefit for nursing home care. That would be referred to as the home care being 100% of what you have as a nursing home benefit. In the example I just used, $160 would be 100%. Some insurers allow you to purchase an at-home benefit of 50% of the nursing home benefit, which in this case would be $80. Insurers may offer additional percentages. In most cases, I'd suggest you choose a home care benefit of 100%, meaning the same dollar benefit as you have for the nursing home. I suggest this because I predict we will have to pay higher wages in the future to home health aides, there will be fewer such workers, and home care services will therefore continue to become more expensive. The AARP Public Policy Institute report projects that there will be a decline in caregiver support by 2030. We are dropping from having perhaps 7 caregivers for each person to only 4 per person. That is concurrent with the rise in population of 80 year olds who will need care. Not a good match-up![24]

4. *Pay-Outs related to daily or monthly expenses?*

The trend is for insurance policies to allow you to gather the costs for many at-home visits together. Look for this feature. It may be a rider for which you pay extra, but it is worth it. If you had a home care benefit of $160 a day, but some days your care cost $300, other times $50, the $160 benefit would not fully cover all the services on a day by day basis, and as a result you might have out of pocket costs. If instead of settling each day's expenses against your maximum daily benefit, you were able to look at the cost of services for the whole month, you might find that, although the charges fluctuated, they did not exceed the daily benefit in this example of $160 times 30 days or $4,800. A pay-out tied to a monthly, not daily, accounting of your service costs might mean that more or all of your services would be paid in full.

5. *Assisted Living*

Look for policies that cover assisted living facilities and will allow you to choose the same dollar amount benefit that you have for the daily nursing home benefit.

6. *Adult Day-Care and Hospice Care*

Your policy should cover these and the daily benefit amount should be the same as the daily benefit amount that you have on at-home care.

7. *How Do I Manage Until the Policy Starts To Pay?*

When should the insurance start and stop paying for services? Logically your answer is "From the minute I need it, until I don't need it anymore." Now we have to see how closely your budget allows you to get to that goal. From a financial planning point of view, the rule of thumb is that you should maintain a reserve of three months of living expenses. If you need $3,500 a month to live on, then the cushion would be about $10,500. That reserve might pay for your own care until the policy starts to pay. So designing the policy to pay on the 61st or the 91st day instead of the 31st day would make the premium lower and would dovetail with the reserve you have already saved.

8. *How Long Should the Policy Pay?*

For your lifetime? For two, four, six, or ten years? Insurance companies vary on the number of years they offer. However, newer policies (2013 on) generally do not offer lifetime benefits. Many will not offer more than six years. From a financial planning perspective, I prefer to see the insurance exist as long as a potential need might exist. The younger you are, the more affordable the policy is and the more years of coverage you may be able to buy.

Insurers may express the benefit that could be paid out to you not in terms of years but in terms of a total benefit reserve, what I referred to as "one bucket." So a daily benefit of $160 multiplied by four years or 1,460 days would be a benefit reserve of $233,600. This makes sense, because if you do not use the maximum each day, it would still be in your pool of money.

9. Empty "Bucket"

What happens when you use up the "bucket of money" that was in your insurance contract? You are then responsible for paying for your own care out of your pocket. Once you have spent your money, if you fit the guidelines for Medicaid, then the government will cover your care. Medicaid is the safety net for people who have no resources.

10. Triggers

What triggers the insurance policy to start paying? That depends on what type of policy you own and what condition you are in. If your policy meets the stipulations of the 1996 Health Insurance Portability and Accountability Act (HIPAA), it is referred to as "Tax Qualified." There will be more about this distinction in the next section. The Tax Qualified policy triggers benefit payments either because of your inability to do certain tasks, or your cognitive impairment. The measurement of your incapacity is that you cannot perform the usual Activities of Daily Living (ADLs) or that you are severely cognitively impaired. A health-care professional must certify that your incapacity is expected to last at least 90 days.

Incapacity generally means that you are unable to do a certain number of ADLs. Often it is any two of the following six activities (in older contracts, it could be two or three out of five ADLs). The ADLs are: bathe yourself, dress yourself, feed yourself, toilet yourself, transfer from a bed to a chair or similar transfer, and/or maintain continence. One way of evaluating whether or not you are incapacitated is that you need someone to be "hands-on;" for example, to actually lift you out of a chair because you cannot get up by yourself.

Another measure of incapacity is that you just need to be watched, for example, walking up the stairs because you are a bit unsteady. This is called "stand-by" assistance. If you need someone only to stand by instead of lift you, you are in better shape, more able to manage on your own. It is better to have a policy that says even if you only need stand-by help, you have lost that ADL. The stand-by assistance concept moves you faster to qualifying for benefits. In most cases, the policy accepts you as incapacitated and ready for benefits once you have lost two ADLs. On the other hand, even if you could perform all the ADLs, you would be considered eligible for benefits if you suffered severe cognitive impairment. Look for a policy with "stand-by" as a measure of incapacity and two of six ADLs.

11. Non-Tax Qualified Offers Another Trigger

There is one more concept called "medically necessary" which is available with some early policies (pre-HIPAA) that are referred to as Non-Tax Qualified (NTQ). This trigger, in some cases, might allow you be eligible for benefits sooner than you would be under the Tax Qualified (TQ) contracts which were discussed in the paragraph above. "Medically necessary" could be very favorable to you. It would allow your physician to recommend care even if you did not fit the stricter guidelines of loss of two ADLs. As you can guess "medically necessary" would be harder to regiment. One doctor's opinion might be more liberal, another's more strict. Many people would shop for doctors who would help them become eligible for benefits sooner. Since 1996, Non-Tax Qualified policies, even though they include "medically necessary," have been in less demand because it is unclear how the payment of the daily benefit would affect your taxes.

Suppose you had a $210 a day benefit and you received care for 100 days. In the non-tax qualified plans it is not clear whether that $21,000 ($210 x 100) would be taxable income in some way. On the other hand, the rules for the Tax Qualified plans assure you that the benefits will not be taxed if you follow the guidelines. The HIPAA 1996 legislation (enacted January 1, 1997) set out the requirements a policy must meet so that a portion of the premium might be eligible for income tax deduction and so that the benefit you would receive if you were on claim would not be taxable. These policies are referred to as Tax Qualified. If you own a Non-Tax Qualified contract, you might want to review whether you should change it to a Tax Qualified contract. Since policies are issued at attained age and evaluate current health, be cautious in making a change.

12. Indemnity or Reimbursement

How does the insurance company pay the claim? Suppose you own a policy that provides for a nursing home benefit of $160 a day. If you have purchased an indemnity plan, the insurer will pay you $160 a day even if the care costs only $150 a day. You are then responsible for paying the nursing home, or other services; if, however, you have a reimbursement plan, the insurer would pay the $150 and the remaining dollars might be banked in the benefit reserve, or "bucket."

If you are in ill health, having to keep track of the indemnity payments may be too much for you. Sadly, there have been reports of people close to the ailing person who took the indemnity checks and used them for other purposes. In most situations, it is preferable to have the reimbursements made directly to the caregivers instead of you.

13. Waiver of premium

When can you stop paying the premium? Waiver of premium is a contract feature that assures you that after a certain number of days during which you are receiving benefits paid for by the insurance company, you do not have to pay the premium. This feature is no longer offered in some newer contracts. However, if you can, choose a policy that applies this waiver to both the care you would receive in a nursing home and at home. Ask. Not all policies waive the premium payment on both. It is valuable to you because you save money. Check the insurer's guidelines for the waiting period for waiver of premium. Does the waiting period start from the first day the insurance company pays for your care, or the first day you receive care that you yourself pay for? This difference could cost you hundreds of dollars. I'll explain that by looking at the next feature, the elimination period. The waiting period for waiver of premium may be added to the elimination period.

14. Elimination period

Another attractive option is being able to satisfy the elimination period just once. Think of it like a deductible on your car insurance. Each time you have a claim, you have to pay the amount of the deductible before the car insurance company compensates you. If you only had to satisfy the deductible once in your lifetime, that would be good news. It would save you money. Such a concept does not apply to car insurance but it does apply to most long-term care insurances. Look for it. Once you have satisfied the elimination period, you never have to do that again.

Some companies are very liberal in allowing you a long time to accumulate the days of the elimination period. This is good for you. In addition, some carriers allow you to speed up the accumulation of days to be credited to fulfill your elimination period by saying that one day of home care will equal seven days. This is like getting double frequent flyer miles or some other bonus. The extra days help you become eligible for benefits sooner.

Policies in the past had elimination periods of zero days, 20 days, 30 days, 90 days, and so on. However, today most do not offer a zero or 20 day elimination period. Companies vary on the exact number of days. If you choose 90 days, you lower the premium. You are picking up the cost of your care for those 90 days.

What is a connection between waiver of

premium #13 and elimination period #14? If your policy has a 90 day elimination period, you would pay for your care during that time. If the waiver of premium is activated after 90 days of your receiving care, then on the 91st day the insurer would start paying for your care and you would stop paying premiums. Good. If instead the waiver of premium is activated after 90 days (the number of days varies among carriers) of your receiving benefits, meaning that the insurer is paying for your care, you would have to pay another three months of premiums. Not as attractive to you.

15. *Inflation Rider*

The younger you are, the more important this rider is. The cost of long-term care continues to increase. So if you buy the right to a room costing $200 today, that same room in 15 years might cost $416 if inflation averaged 5%. Wouldn't you like your policy to keep up? If you had a 5% compound inflation rider, you would be able to pay for the $416 room in that example. The other inflation riders like 3% simple or 5% simple, would not "grow" your ability to pay for the room as quickly as a compound inflation rider would. Riders with simple inflation are generally less expensive riders and do help adjust for some inflation, but perhaps not enough.

A simple inflation rider would add the same dollar amount for 15 years, meaning that $200 a day times 5% is $10. Each year you add the same ten dollars, and at the end of 15 years you would be able to pay for a $340 room. So, if you are age 65 or under and can afford the compound inflation rider, that is a good choice. The compound inflation rider has a better chance of keeping up with the actual increasing cost of long-term care. If you are over age 65, the simple inflation rider may be more affordable. The policies also offer the choice of a cost-of-living adjusted rider, but this is offered in a pattern that may not help keep the policy current with rising long-term care costs. No rider available now guarantees that it will inflate your policy's daily benefit at the same rate that long-term care increases. One defensive measure can be to purchase at the outset a benefit that is 5% to 10% more than the average daily rates in your area. Inflation adjustment is one of the more expensive aspects of the contract. If you can grow the value of other assets in your portfolio, you could perhaps choose the least expensive inflation rider or none at all.

Other inflation questions to ask include: If you were on claim, would the inflation benefit continue? When you are off claim, meaning you are no longer in need of receiving benefits, does the inflation rider start with the original dollar amount for the room or does it inflate what remains, in other words, pick up from the highest number it was before you went on claim? The latter is more favorable for you. Otherwise, it is as if your use of the policy when you were on claim has set you back.

16. Discounts

There are discounts with some carriers for you and your spouse applying together. If one of you is not well enough to be insured, the other one may still qualify for the discount. Other carriers will not give a discount unless both apply and are insured. There are also discounts for two related people living together, for example, two sisters, for married same sex couples and common law "marriages." Ask also about good health discounts. You may qualify for the best rating which would lower your premium.

17. First Death

After the death of the first spouse, some carriers will consider the policy of the surviving spouse to be paid up. The carriers vary on their guidelines. One example is if the policies were in force for a number of years and there were no claims, then the survivor's policy would be paid up. With some "shared" policies, the surviving spouse could access unused benefits of the policy of the deceased.[25]

18. Travel

If you often travel outside the United States, inquire whether or not the policy would pay for care when you are away, how much of your benefit would it cover and for how long. Some Medicare supplement polices (Medigap) cover international travel, but only for what Medicare would cover in the United States. If you travel a lot consider applying for an international health insurance plan.[26]

19. Care Specialist

Is there a Geriatrics Care Specialist or a Care Coordinator who will help you and your family access help in your community and make the best use of your benefits? Is this service charged against your "bucket" of money? Do you need to satisfy the elimination period to have the service? "No" for the last two questions is the better answer for you.[27]

20. Bed Reservation

Does the bed reservation apply to non-medical absences from the nursing home as well as hospitalizations? This means that the nursing home will reserve your bed for you for a certain number of days whether you are away from the nursing home because you had to go to the hospital or because you are going to be with family for holidays or vacation.

21. Return of Premium

What if you buy this type of policy but never have a claim? Insurance is a safety net. Its best value is that it is there ready to catch you if you fall into trouble. I hope you never need it. Nonetheless, if you would like the premium dollars back, or want your beneficiary to receive the premium dollars you paid in, there are some policies that are designed to give back the premium dollars in very specific situations. Suppose someone bought the policy at age 50 (as recommended) but died in a terrible accident at 64, then all the premiums paid in would go to the beneficiary. That is one version of return of premium. Ask if the insurer offers this provision and how it is structured. The possibility of the returned premium dollars may be enough incentive for you to proceed with the purchase.

22. Restrictions

What restrictions are there on the policy? Some are standard, such as the policy does not cover treatment, services or confinement due to self-inflicted injury or attempted suicide. Check that the restrictions do not mention something important to you like coverage when you travel abroad.

23. Tax Advantages

For the 2014 tax filing, if you itemize medical expense deductions for Schedule A (Form 1040), then you can claim a portion of the premium you paid for a **qualified** long-term care insurance contract, for instance, Age 60 to 70 up to $3,720, Age 71 and over $4,600. (See item 11 about non-tax qualified.)[28]

24. The Insurance Company

Some questions you want to ask are: how long has the insurance company been offering long-term care insurance? This type of policy has been offered since about 1960, and few current companies have that longevity. Experience counts, as does a long-term commitment to the market by that insurance carrier. What indicates that the insurer will stay in that line of business? This is hard to answer. But you may want to call the insurer's toll-free phone number to get answers from the person who heads the division on long-term care. You could talk to the insurer's marketing department. You might look at an annual financial report to see if the company derives a significant percent of its profits from this line of insurance. If so, then it is critical that this division be successful. Ask if the company has made any innovations in its long-term care policies and if it was the first in the business to do so. Such innovation suggests that the company is committing dollars to research and analysis on how to make its offerings really competitive.

Look at their marketing material. Is it helpful to you as a consumer? Are there knowledgeable people on their toll-free phone line to answer your questions? What is the financial strength of the insurance company that will underwrite your policy? There are several agencies that rate the strength of insurance companies. You are looking for companies that are rated excellent, superior, strong, and good. These are not just praiseworthy adjectives. They are an evaluation of the company's financial situation. The specific ratings for Standard and Poor's, Moody's and A.M. Best are in an endnote to this article.[29]

WASTED MONEY?

If you are still saying to yourself, "What if I buy it and never use it?" consider buying a life insurance policy with a long-term care rider or an annuity with a long-term care benefit. These are approaches that will provide some long-term care protection and you will not have "wasted your money." If you continue to feel that you would have wasted your money if you never had a long-term care claim, compare that with auto or home insurance. If you never had a claim, would you feel that you had wasted your money? If you did not have insurance, and your home had to be completely rebuilt because of a fire, where would the money come from? If your car was totaled and you had no insurance, what would happen?

Despite the statistics that indicate there is a 70% chance that after age 65 you may need long-term care in some form for about three years,[30] you may not be persuaded to buy insurance. You're going to risk being in the 30% who are untouched. Yes, an optimistic view is laudable, **if** you have a plan to help protect the downside.

Let's address this mindset of "getting your money's worth." In addition to the stand alone long-term care insurance, there are two other approaches to creating a layer of downside protection. These are two types of combination products: life insurance with a long-term care rider, and annuities with a long-term care benefit.

LIFE INSURANCE AND LONG-TERM CARE

If you have loved ones you want to help protect, or any debt, then the purchase of life insurance with a long-term care rider might be able to solve the problem of paying for long-term care. The death benefit would be drawn down to care for you. Whatever was left would go to your beneficiaries. If you never needed long-term care, the full death benefit might help pay off a mortgage, estate settlement costs, other debts, or it could take care of a surviving spouse, other loved ones or special charities. Not dying is not an option, so you get your money's worth either in your care or in your taking care of others.

As you might guess, various life insurers are experimenting with meeting the needs of the consumer while they are vigilant on the actuarial side. They do have to stay in business and be healthy to pay your claims. John Hancock, which has been innovative, is one of a number of insurers that provides the life and long-term care combination. These policies are structured so that you would pay an annual, quarterly, or monthly premium for the life insurance. However, instead of periodic payments, a variation is investing a lump sum into a life insurance contract which then would pay out for long-term care, and/or a death benefit. You might look at Lincoln's Money Guard, and State Farm with Annuity Care.

Before you do that review, do check the life insurance contract you may already own. It may not be one of these newer types, but it very likely has an acceleration of death benefit feature. This is triggered by a diagnosis of terminal illness, whereas a long-term care rider comes into play when you are unable to perform the activities of daily living. If you have a fatal diagnosis, you can choose to have part of the death benefit paid out to cover the current costs of care. Alternatively, the death benefit would be paid to your beneficiaries.

ANNUITIES AND LONG-TERM CARE

The annuity and long-term care combination has several versions. One **adds income**. It is a variable annuity built to contribute to your retirement income. The other type of annuity, a fixed annuity **stores value**. It is designed to store value and only pay out for long-term care, or death. Both types typically require a lump sum to be deposited. How much you invest depends on your assets and on how much of a payout you want.

Adds Income: Suppose you invested $100,000 in this type of variable annuity. (Minimums are generally about $25,000, maximums one million.) It is a long-term investment which has two components: a living benefit and a cash value. The cash value rides up and down with the markets. You are familiar with that in your retirement plans. The other component, however, provides guarantees. The living benefit guarantees a specific rate of return, and a promise from the insurer that whatever gains are achieved cannot be lost or decline. These guarantees are backed by the insurance company and not FDIC insured. There are specific guidelines for when and how you take distributions. For a more thorough discussion, please read my white paper, *"Annuities: Retirement Guarantees-Promises or Traps"* available at www.wealthychoices.com.

It is recommended to have this sort of annuity grow for 5 or more years to build up the living benefit. Then when you want to start the distributions, you can receive regular payments for your whole life, even if you live past 100. Suppose during the time you are receiving income, if you need the services of a nursing home, then the annuity with a nursing home rider would pay out more. How much more depends on the specific insurance company's contract. The important point is that you have more cash on hand to pay for your care. If you never need long-term care, you can continue to receive income from the annuity.

You have invested money and you are receiving income and perhaps additional income for the time you might be in a nursing home. Yes, each insurance contract is different. My purpose here is to introduce the concept not to detail all the variations. One company you can review is Transamerica.

The other type of annuity **Stores Value.** Suppose you invest $100,000 in this sort of annuity; you are counting on the insurer to leverage your investment increasing it in value. IF you should need long-term care, the contract would pay out income for a period of time, generally for six years or less. How much money you would receive and how long you would receive it are a function of how much you invested, your health rating and your age. At your death, if you did not have a long-term care claim, your beneficiary would benefit. My intent is to provide a broad overview, not to detail the specifics of how each company works. There is a lot for you to learn about these contracts. One of the companies offering this variation is Forethought's Forecare.

KEY DIFFERENCES

You should be aware of some significant differences in the three approaches.

Inflation

The costs of nursing homes and of health care in general are rising faster than the consumer price index, or what we often call inflation. Therefore, an advantage to a stand-alone long-term care policy is that it can be designed so the benefit paid out to you, if and when it is needed, keeps up with inflation. If the national average for a private room in nursing home today costs $250 [31] and if inflation were to average 3% over 20 years, then that daily rate might rise to about $452. Your contract could be designed to keep up with that. You may be able to adjust for 3% or 5% inflation. Ask specifically about the inflation escalation with these approaches. Lincoln's Money Guard allows for some choices for inflation which in turn, reduce the death benefit and long-term care benefit.

Settings for Care

Does the contract pay out in all settings: nursing home, at home and assisted living? The long-term care provision in Transamerica's annuity is only for care in a nursing home.

Length of Payout

Note that variable annuities with living benefits like Transamerica's do pay income for your retirement life time, or for your life and for that of your spouse. The long-term care increase may be only for a set number of years.

For each of the types of coverage (stand-alone long-term care, or combination life and long-term care, or annuity and long-term care), check how long the long-term care benefit lasts.

One More Variation

Insuring for long-term care is a dynamic discussion with you, the consumer, the insurance company, the actuaries, and the medical profession. We are living longer and healthier lives. However, as we move into our 80's we are likely to be in need of care for a variety of reasons. "One in 8 Americans over the age of 65 has Alzheimer's, and the disease affects 42.5% of Americans over the age of 85." [32]

A New Idea

Short-term Care Insurance is a relatively new "recovery" of expenses, or critical care insurance. It could help reimburse you for a short nursing home stay, or for at home care. It could help protect your assets to that extent. You would need to qualify for the coverage.

It is not standardized, and also not available as of this writing in New York, California, Massachusetts, Florida, Vermont, New Hampshire, Rhode Island, Connecticut, and Minnesota. [33] It is designed to cover you for less than 12 months for daily amounts from $50 to $300. It could cover the waiting period for a traditional long-term care contract, or fill in for what your health insurance or Medicare do not cover. As with long-term care, the benefit is triggered by failing to be able to manage 2 of 6 activities of daily living, or if you are failing cognitively. [34]

For those who need some protection and cannot afford traditional long-term care, cannot qualify for life insurance, do not have lump sums to invest in an annuity, this new product may be a partial solution.

SUMMARY

In all of these combination products, your money is "not being wasted." The particular companies are representative of those taking new approaches. Expect that more and different versions will be designed.

You can create a layer of protection for long-term care with the stand alone long-term care insurance policy, or life with long-term care, or an annuity with long-term care. Is one approach better than another? Yes. The best approach needs to be created for your unique situation. There isn't one answer for everyone.

Understanding the impact of health care costs

during retirement is as important as working to maximize income and managing investment risk. However, many financial advisors may not be up to speed on Medicare, Medicaid, Social Security, disability income, or long-term care, so they may not cover these areas. A financial plan that does not address these issues is a like setting sail in a leaking boat. Please don't do that. Take the time to learn and to make good decisions for your situation.

CONCLUSION

If reading this guide has given you confidence and a procedure for thinking out a complex issue, it has been a good use of your time. You may want to ask for help from other advisors to analyze long-term care insurance contracts, to position your assets for an appropriate retirement plan, to review your taxes and tax strategies for both income taxes and estate taxes, and to draft the necessary legal documents. If you take these steps, you will have a better grasp of the issues and feel more in control.[35]

Remember, the sooner you take action, the more and better choices you are likely to have. So give yourself a deadline of two weeks to a month to make your decision about how you will address the drain of long-term care, and then begin taking care of the related issues that we have talked about.

Whatever your decision—to own or not own such insurance—you have a road map that explains what you need to take care of. Making progress in putting things in order is very liberating. It reduces stress about the unknown and gives you a sense of well-being. You can congratulate yourself for taking care of what you reasonably could take care of. Live well. Live long. Enjoy your loved ones. Shakespeare tells us, "to love that well which thou must leave ere long."

Wishing you health, prosperity and wealthy choices. Thanks for the opportunity of having this conversation with you. I'll be listening for your response.

Resources

Please note as you check books on the topic of long-term care that the HIPAA 1996 legislation which was effective as of January 1997 changed the landscape for the long-term care insurance policies and the financial and legal advice around long-term care. You will want to be sure the writer has incorporated the new information. There are many fine books and articles. This handful will get you started.

LIVE TO 120

VISUAL IMPACT

- **How I Would Like to Be When I am 70** by Vladimir Yakovlev. Also available at www.facebook.com/theageofhappiness and available through www.earthporm.com/age-happiness-60-older-seniors-will-destroy-age-stereotypes. This is a collection of photographs and stories of active people 60 to over 100 that reframe what is possible.

- **One Hundred Over 100: Moments With One Hundred North American Centenarians** by Jim Heymen. Photographs by Paul Boyer (Golden, Colorado: Fulcrum Publishing, 1990). This book shows that age is a just a number, not a limit.

FROM A SCIENCE PERSPECTIVE:

- **Aging With Attitude: Growing Older With Dignity and Vitality** by Robert Levine, MD (Westport, Connecticut: Praeger, 2004). Dr Levine includes stories of his patients' success as he discusses the changes in our bodies, common diseases that affect the elderly, ways to deal with ageism and the opportunities of the new millennium.

- **The Anti-aging Plan: Stay Younger Longer** by Marios Kyriazis, MD. (Boston: Element Ltd., 2000). The doctor believes that it is biologically possible to live to a healthy 120. He provides guidance to help you take better care of yourself.

- **Aging Well: Surprising Guideposts to a Happier Life from the Landmark Harvard Study,** George Valliant (Boston: Little, Brown, 2008). This is a study by Harvard Medical School that followed 824 men from teens to old age. Valliant summarizes key lessons from the study in an article for *Greater Good*, Oct. 23, 2013: "... success in relationships was very highly correlated with both economic success and strong mental and physical health... In short, it was the history of warm intimate relationships—and the ability to foster them in maturity—that predicted flourishing in all aspects of these men's lives."

- **Cheating Death: The Promise and the Future Impact of Trying to Live Forever** by Marvin Cetron and Owen Davies (New York: St. Martin's Press, 1998). Because science has made breakthroughs in understanding the process of aging, it will be possible to live to over 100 and retain the vigor of middle age. The authors look into the future with us and discuss the social, religious and financial implications of long life.

- **Great Good Science Center** www.greatgood. berkeley.edu The mission of this website is to study the psychology, sociology, and neuro-science of well-being, and to teach skills that foster, a thriving, resilient, and compassionate society. One recommended article is "Does Happiness Really Help You Live Longer?" by Emiliana R. Simon-Thomas.

THE ADVICE FROM THE SAGES:

- **The Gift of Years: Growing Older Gracefully** by Joan Chittister (New York: Blue Bridge, 2008). Chittister, now in her 70's, writes in the introduction, "It is time for us to let go of both our fantasies of eternal youth and our fears of getting older, and to find the beauty of what it means to age well" (p.10).

- **The Oxford Book of Aging: Reflections of the Journey of Life,** edited by Thomas R. Cole and Mary G. Winkler (New York: Oxford, 1994. This is a gathering of poems and short passages on aging from many centuries.

- **The Secrets of Happiness: Three Thousand**

Years of Searching for the Good Life, Richard Schoch (New York: Scribner, 2006). Schoch provides a perspective on happiness by studying the wisdom of ancient and modern writers.

- **30 Lessons for Living: Tried and True Advice from the Wisest Americans**, by Karl Pillemer (New York: Hudson Street Press, 2011). This book is full of inspiring and funny comments from people you would like to have as neighbors.

VERY PRACTICAL ADVICE:

- Guide to Organizations and Services. Consulting a trained librarian and/or searching the internet will help you find associations that focus on particular illnesses, and services of all sorts that help elders. The following websites highlight types of services from which you can build your research: Billing paying services, American Association of Daily Money Managers, www.AADMM.com
- Geriatric care managers, www.aginglifecare.org

- Elder care attorneys, www.naela.org

The following books cover topics from caregiving to emotions to moving to care facilities:

- **How to Care for Aging Parents: A One-Stop Resource for All Your Medical, Financial, Housing and Emotional Issues,** 3rd ed. by Virginia Morris (New York: Workman Publishing, 2014).
- **Stages of Senior Care: Your Step-by-Step Guide to Making the Best Decisions**, by Paul and Lori Hogan (New York: McGraw Hill, 2009).

End Notes

1   "Long-term care information: Introduction" CSU-ERFA. http://csuerfa.org/long-term-care.html.

2   Commission on Long-Term Care, Report to the Congress, (Sept. 30, 2013), p.3.

3   Family Caregiver Alliance, "Selected Long-Term Care Statistics: Who needs Long-Term Care: Family and Informal Caregivers" (https://Caregiver.org updated February 2015).

4   Commission on Long-Term Care, p.3.

5   Ibid., p.5.

6   Ibid, Family Caregiver Alliance.

7   NYS Robert Wood Johnson Project, in Journal of American Society of CLU & ChFC. Nov. 1997.

8   Managed Care Digest: Long-Term Care (Kansas City, MO, Marion Merrell Dow, 1992), quoted in Older Americans Almanac: A Reference Work on Seniors in the US, ed. Ronald J Manheimer (Gale, 1994), p. 581.

9   "Who provides Long-Term Care in the U. S.? The SCAN Foundation, Fact sheet, October 2012. (www. TheSCANFoundation.org).

10   Commission on Long-term Care, p.12. Rand Corporation Survey 10-27, 2014, finds that friends and family provide caregiving that has a value of $522 billion, whereas formal paid care is $221 billion. Journal Health Services Research. Ibid. Family Caregiver Alliance details some of the costs to the caregivers: they had to decrease their work hours, declined taking

a promotion, took a leave of absence, quit their jobs. Their personal health suffered from increased coronary heart disease, elevated blood pressure, poorer immune function.

[11]   Ibid. Who Provides Long –Term Care in the U.S.?

[12]   See the video of the Robot R70i at www.genworth.com. Play with the controls and see how our bodies change.

[13]   The annual national median cost of care for a private room in a nursing home is $91,250. The lowest is $60,225 in Oklahoma, with the northeastern states coming in at over $100,000 with Connecticut the highest at $158,775. *Genworth Cost of Care Survey 2015*, pp. 5, 19. The national average hourly pay for a private duty nurse is $35.99, which for a year's worth of 24 hour care would run $315,272. www.salaryexpert.com.

[14]   "2016 SSI and Spousal Impoverishment Standards" Medicaid. gov/medicasl-chip-program-information/bytopics/eligibility/downloads/2016-SSI_and spousalimpoverishment-standards.pdf.

[15]   *Genworth 2015 Cost of Care Survey*, p.7 (www.genworth.com).

[16]   Ibid. Commission on Long-Term Care p. 24.

[17]   *Genworth 2015 Cost of Care Survey*, p. 19. New York average private room annually is $136,437, and Connecticut, the highest average, is $158,775.

[18]   No specific investment is intended in this hypothetical example. The arithmetic is to help you compare the order of magnitude of what you might be able to save against the cost of care.

[19]   The break-even analysis is a hypothetical. It does not account for any increase in the premium for the insurance policy, nor can it predict that the cost of the nursing home will go up by 3%. The example provides a comparison of what you might have paid out and the benefit you might receive.

[20]   Ibid. *Genworth 2015 Cost of Care Survey*, p. 4.

21   These hypothetical numbers are intended to give a concrete example and do not refer to any specific investments.

22   American Association for Long-term Care Insurance.

23   Unpublished research of Glenn Cadigan, Total Care Associates, Andover, MA.

24   Ibid. Commission on Long-term Care, pp.13-14.

25   Long-term care policies continue to change. If you need help reviewing an older policy of a friend or relative, call the insurance company and ask them to explain whatever is not clear to you. You can also contact any financial advisor who is familiar with the contracts. You also have my number 800 631 1970. Don't fret. There is help.

26   Two of the many international medical insurance companies to consider are Petersen's International (www.piu.org, 800 345 8816 in California) and International Medical Group (www.imglobal.com/en/index.aspx, 1 866 368 3724).

27   New versions of long-term care contracts come out, so check for the new provisions and ideas.

28   www.irs.gov/publications/p502/ar02.html. This information is not intended to be a substitute for specific individualized tax advice. We suggest that you discuss your specific tax issues with a qualified tax advisor.

29   Favorable ratings are: Standard & Poor's: AAA = Extremely Strong; AA = Very Strong; A = Strong; BBB = Good Moody: Aaa=Exceptional; Aa=Excellent; A=Good; Baa = Adequate A.M. Best: A++, A+ = Superior; A, A- = Excellent; B++, B+ = Very Good; B, B- = Good

30   U.S. Department of Health & Human Services. National Clearinghouse for Long-term Care Information. http://www.longtermcare.gov/the-basics.

31   Genworth Cost of Care Survey 2015, p.5.

[32]   Commission on Long-term Care, Report to Congress, Sept. 30, 2013, p.9.

[33]   http://www.shorttermcareinsurance.org/state-availability.html August, 2015.

[34]   Raymond Smith, "New Short Term Care Insurance; Why did I buy it for myself?" http://www.seniorresourcesguide.com/articles/art01238.html. The opinions voiced in this material are for general information only and are not intended to provide specific advice or recommendations for any individual. All performance referenced is historical and is no guarantee of future results. All guarantees are based on the claims paying ability of the issuer. Riders are additional guarantee options that are available to an annuity or life insurance contract holder. While some riders are part of an existing contract, many others may carry additional fees, charges and restrictions, and the policy holder should review their contract carefully before purchasing. Variable annuities are long-term, tax-deferred investment vehicles designed for retirement purposes and contain both an investment and insurance component. They have fees and charges, including mortality and expense risk charges, administrative fees, and contract fees. They are sold only by prospectus. Withdrawals made prior to age 59 are subject to 10% IRS penalty tax, and surrender charges may apply. Gains from tax-deferred investments are taxable as ordinary income upon withdrawal. The investment returns and principal value of the available sub-account portfolios will fluctuate so that the value of an investor's unit, when redeemed, may be worth more or less than their original value.

[35]   There are many worthwhile organizations, but here are two to help you get started in your search. Reviewing their websites could help you formulate your questions and learn more about what support is available. There are two groups that can help you find professionals in your area—the first is for those who specialize in the care of older people and the second is the

lawyers who would be most knowledgeable about Medicare, Medicaid, Trusts, Special Needs, etc. Geriatric care managers, www.aginglifecare.org. Before 2013, this organization was known as National Association of Professional Geriatric Care Managers. 520-881-8008 in Arizona. www.aginglifecare.org. National Academy of Elder Law Attorneys. 703-942-5711. www.naela.org.

Penelope Tzougros, PhD, ChFC, CLU

"The art of wealth begins by asking the right questions about your money and yourself. The better the questions, the better the answers, the better the results." The better you and I communicate about your values, worries, concerns, goals and timelines, the more suitable and individualized your financial plan will be. It will be flexible and make sense to you. You and I have the same goal of wanting you to have—on your terms—a creative, secure and satisfying retirement.

In 1986, after serving for thirteen years as a professor in New York and Boston, I joined Bay Financial Associates as a financial planner. Wanting to reach a national audience with my seminars, books, radio and television shows, I established Wealthy Choices® in 2000. For updates on teleseminars, books, free whitepapers, and other resources, please check www.wealthychoices.com.

I specialize now on retirement income; how to turn whatever you have accumulated into income for life. Questions you generally need answers to are how to deal with Social Security, long-term care, your legacy, Medicare and the insurances related to Medicare, inflation and sufficient income and growth in your portfolio. A plan that addresses these issues in a helpful way can give you more confidence to face those hopefully happy and healthy retirement years.

Thank you for reading this pocket guide. For your sake, think through the issues and make the best decision for you. Don't wait until circumstances take away your choices, and make the decision for you. Decide, then go out and celebrate life.

I'm here to help. Just give me a call, or send an email.

Yasou!

NOTES

NOTES

NOTES

NOTES